NOPQRSTUVWXYZ

NOPQRSTUVWXYZ

NOPQRSTUVWXYZ

NOPQRSTUVWXYZ

NOPQRSTUVWXYZ

NOPQRSTUVWXYZ

NOPQRSTUVWXYZ

NOPQRSTUVWXYZ

NOPQRSTUVWXYZ

NOPQRSTUVWXYZ

W9-AHI-223

STILL ANOTHER ALPHABET BOOK

ABCDEFGHIJKLMNOPQRSTUVWXYZ

by Seymour Chwast and Martin Stephen Moskof

This alphabet book is also a puzzle and a game. Look carefully at the alphabet at the bottom of each page. Can you find the word that describes the picture? If you can't, you'll find the answer at the back of the book.

McGraw-Hill Book Company   New York   Toronto   London   Sydney

No part of this work may be reproduced without the permission of the publisher.
All Rights Reserved. Printed and bound in Belgium by
Offset Printing, Van Den Bossche S. A. ☒
Library of Congress Catalog Card Number: 70-80968.

**This Book
Is Dedicated To**
Alvin
Bea
Caroline
Daniel
Eve
Florence
Gwendolyn
Heidi
Isadore
Judy
Kathy
Leo
Mark
Nancy
Ovid
Pamela
Quincy
Robert
Saki
Tondeleo
Ursula
Viola
Wayne
Xavier
Yvonne
Zorba

ABCDEFGHIJKLMNOPQRSTUVWXYZ

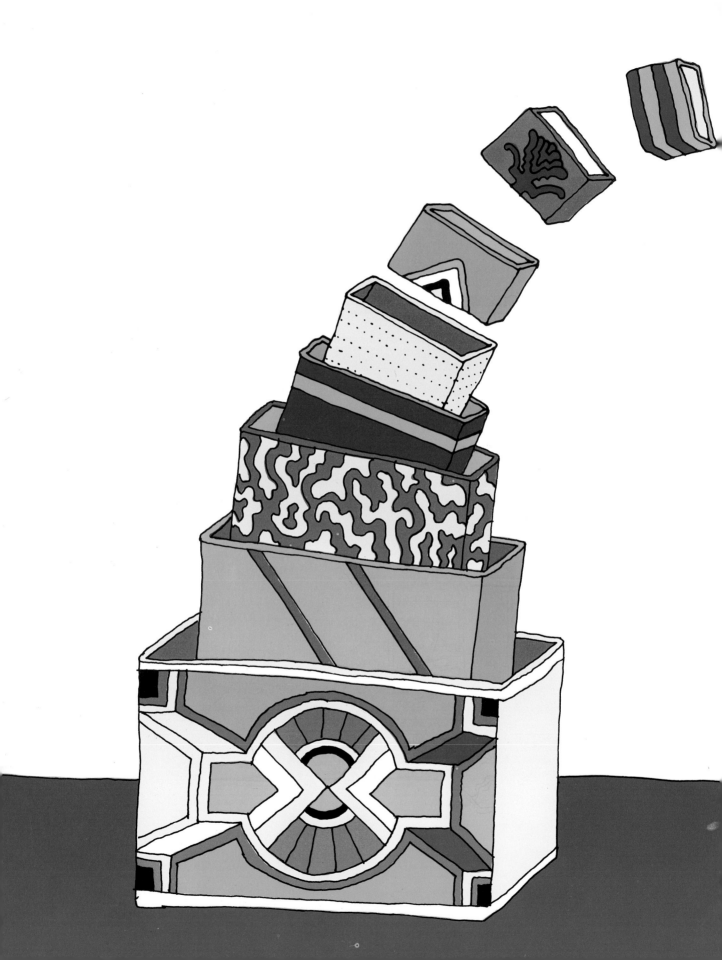

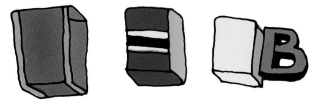

ABCDEFGHIJKLMNOPQRSTUVWXYZ

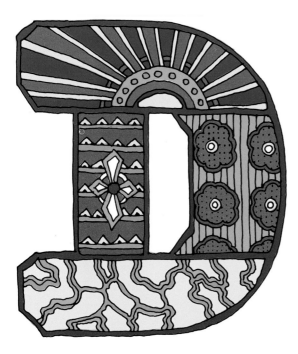
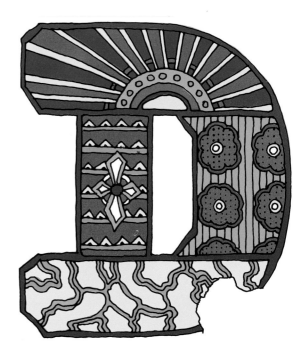

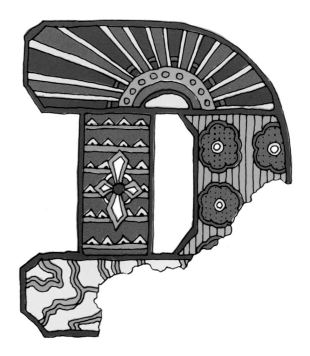

ABCDEFGHIJKLMNOPQRSTUVWXYZ

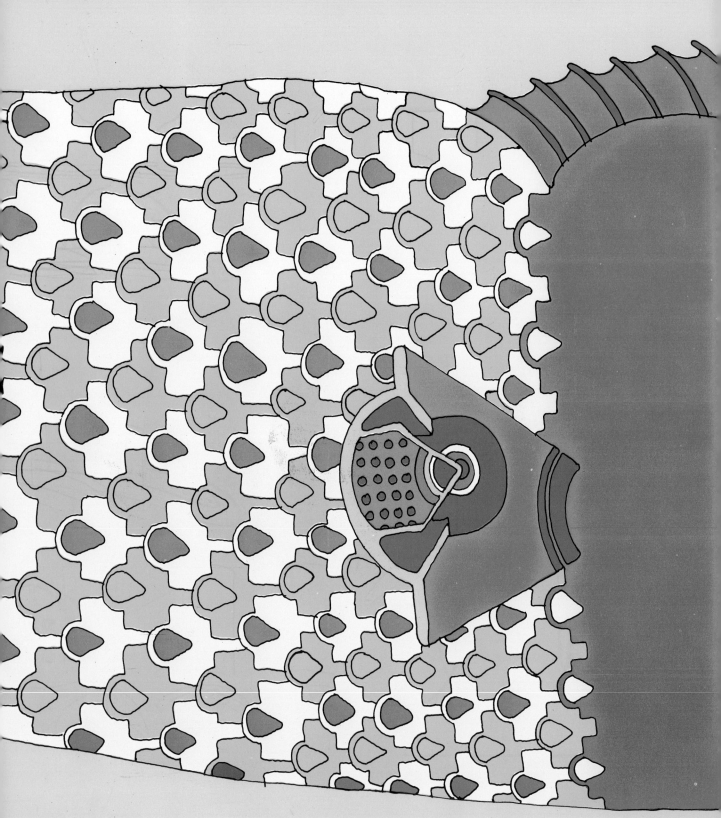

ABCDE FGHIJKLMNOPQRSTUVWXYZ

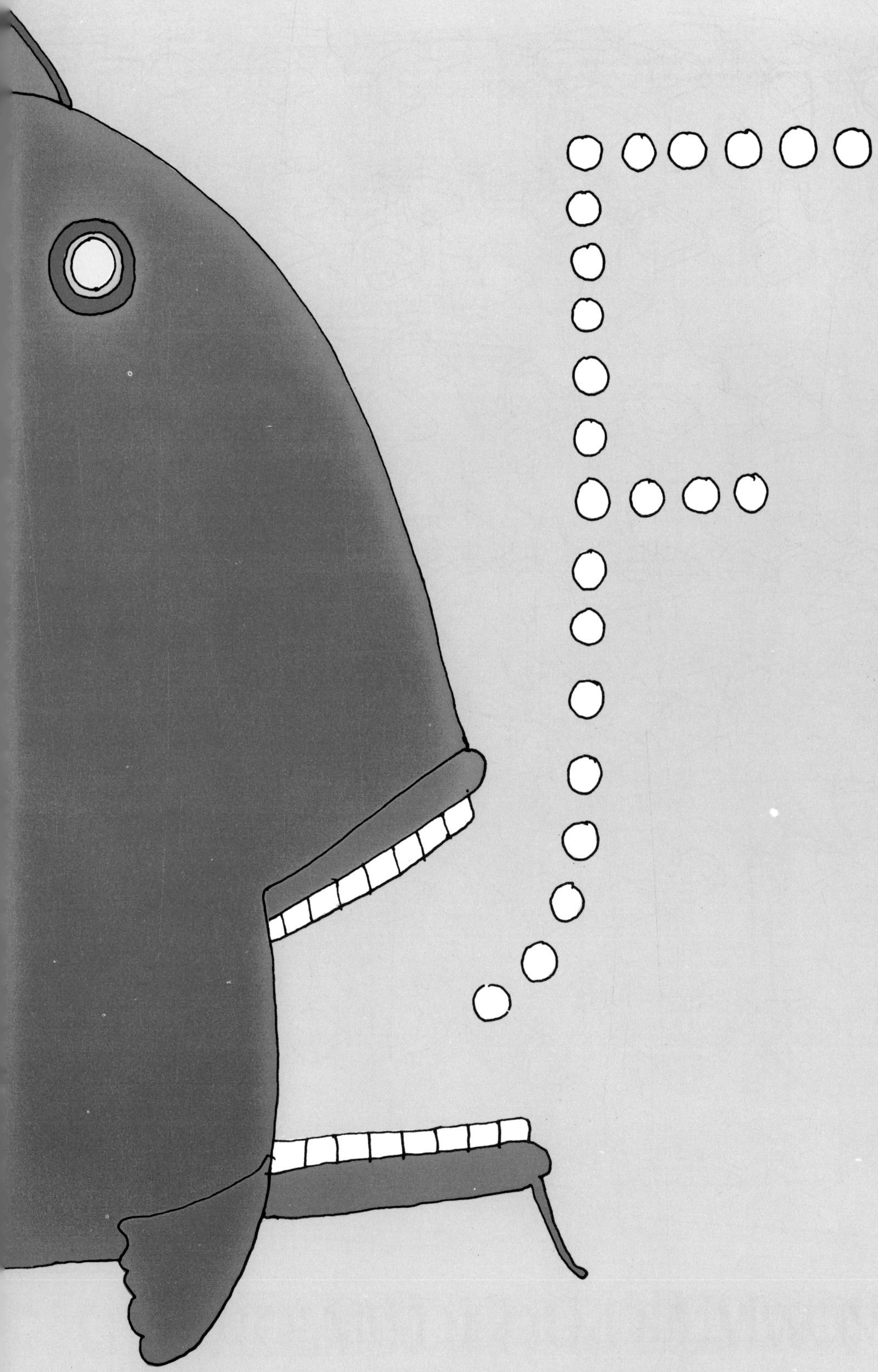

ABCDEFGHIJKLM

NOPQRSTUVWXYZ

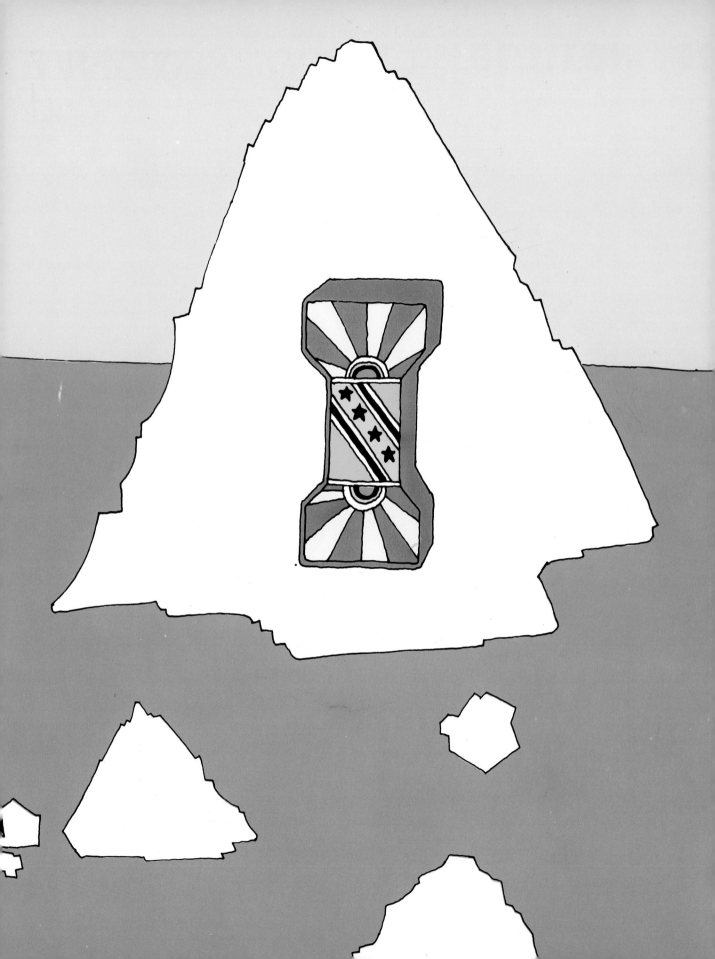

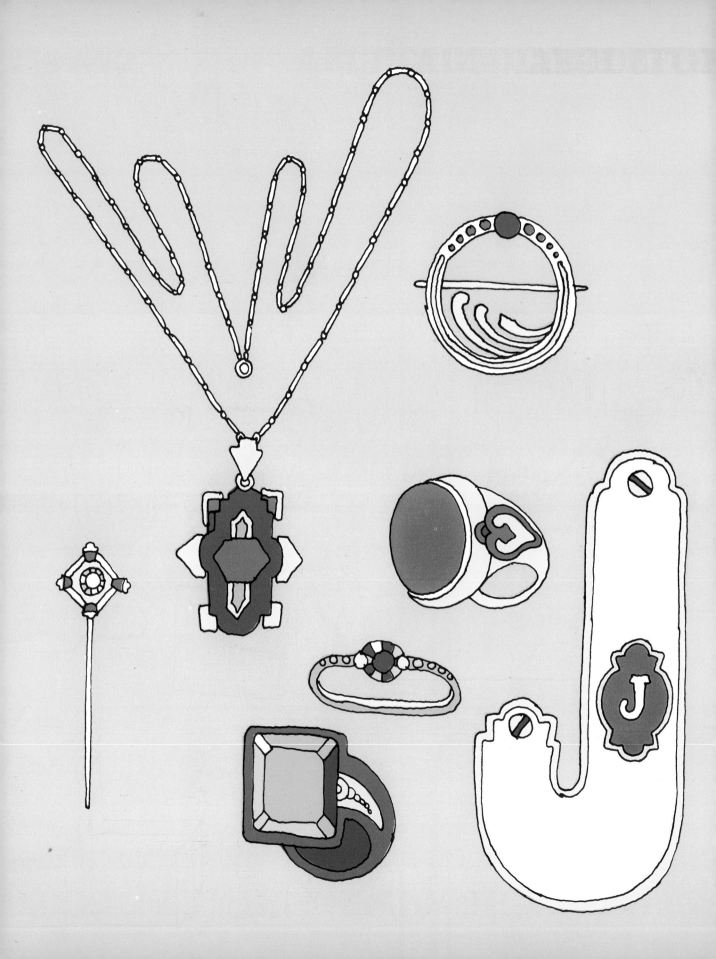

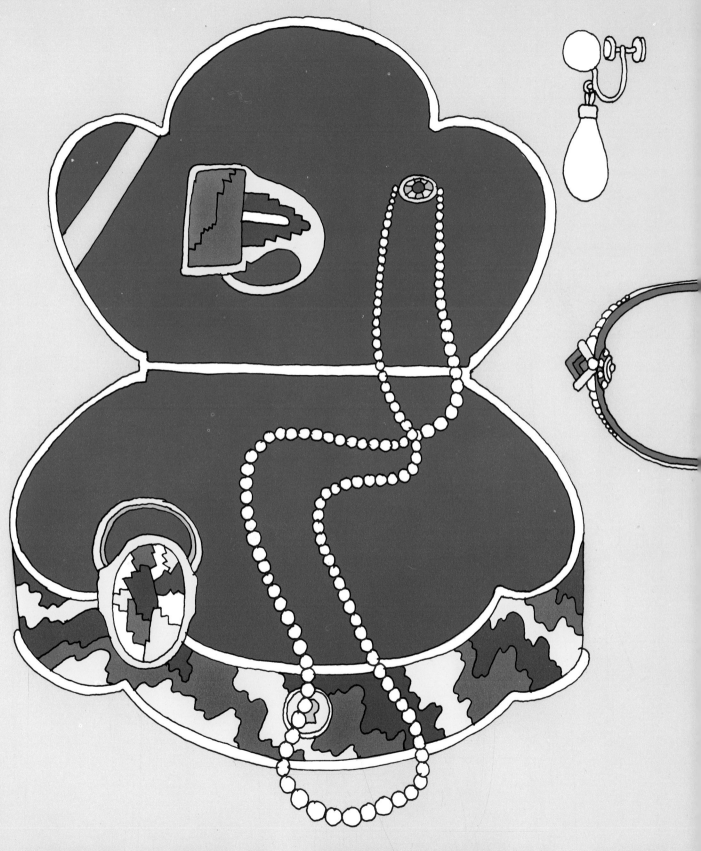

ABCDEFGHIJKLMNOPQRSTUVWXYZ

ABCDEF**GHIJ**K**LM**NOPQRSTUVWXYZ

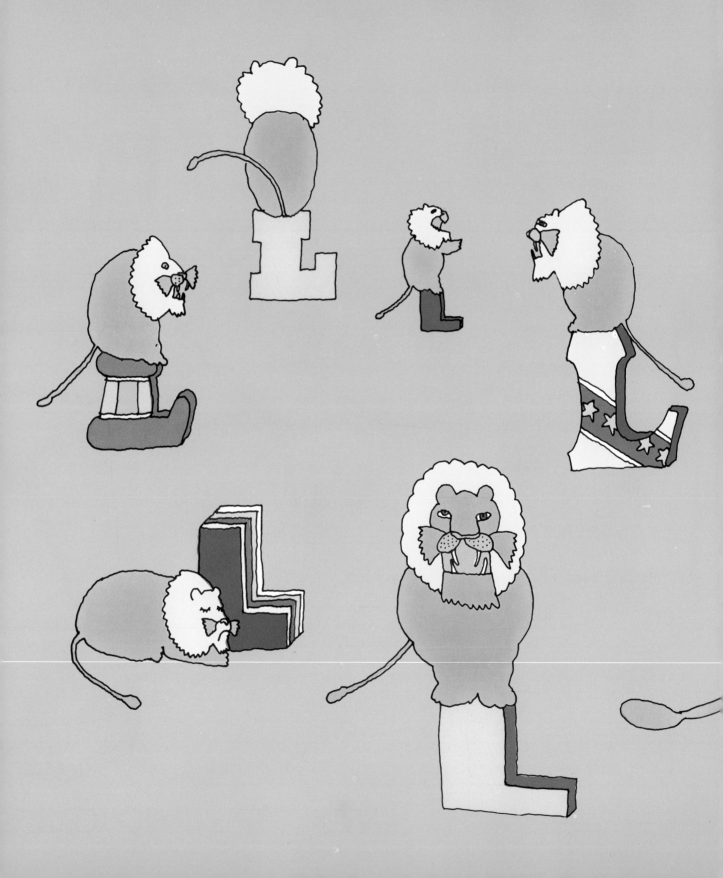

ABCDEFGHIJKLM

NOPQRSTUVWXYZ

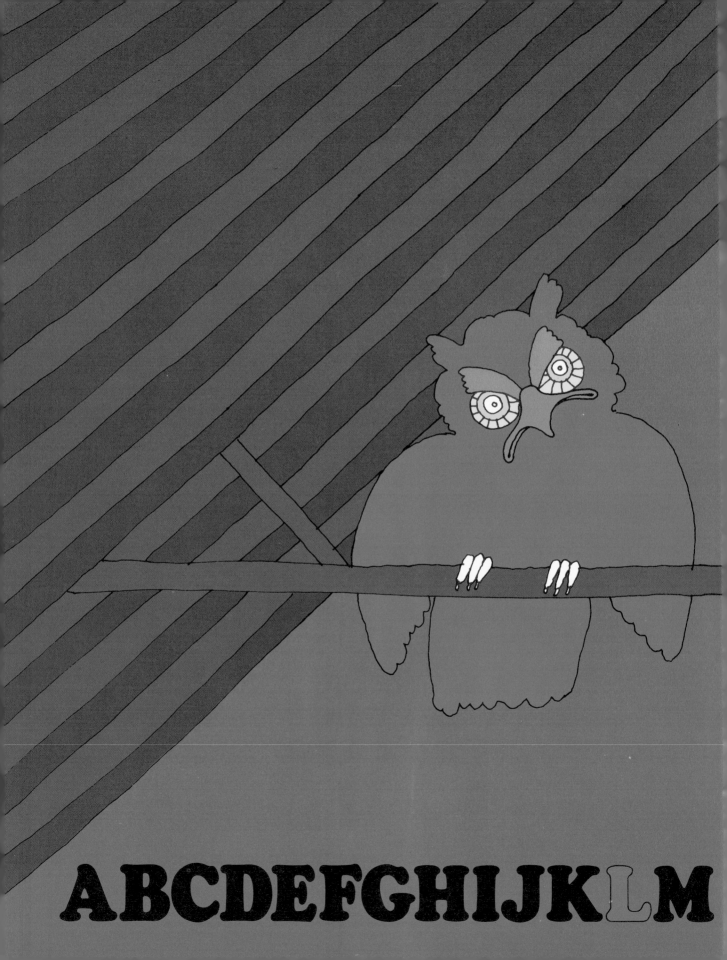

ABCDEFGHIJKLM

NOPQRSTUVWXYZ

ABCD*E*FG*H**I*JKLMNO*P*QRSTUVWXYZ

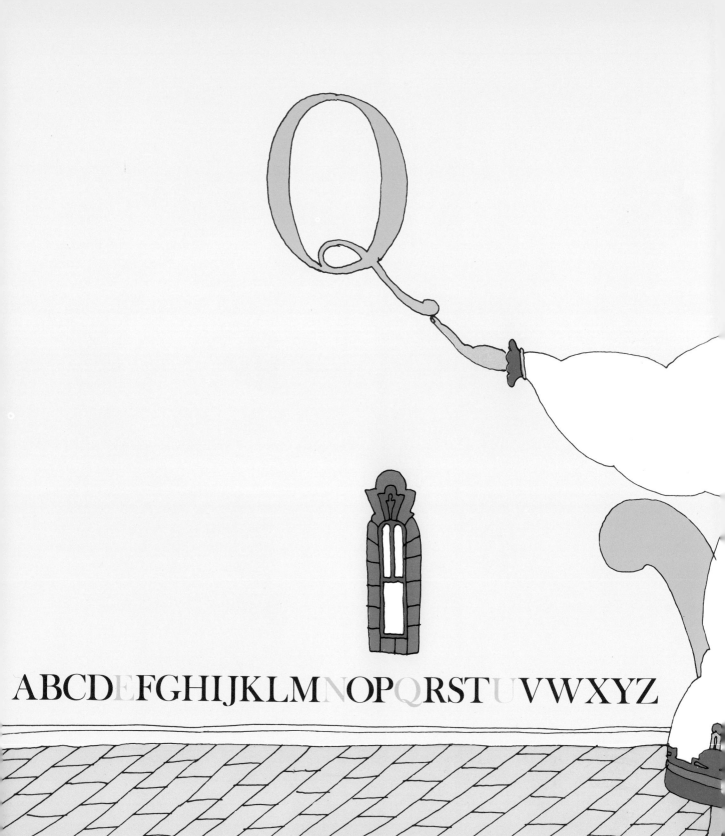

ABCDEFGHIJKLMNOPQRSTUVWXYZ

ABCDEFGHIJKLMNOPQRSTUVWXYZ

ABCDEFGHIJKL

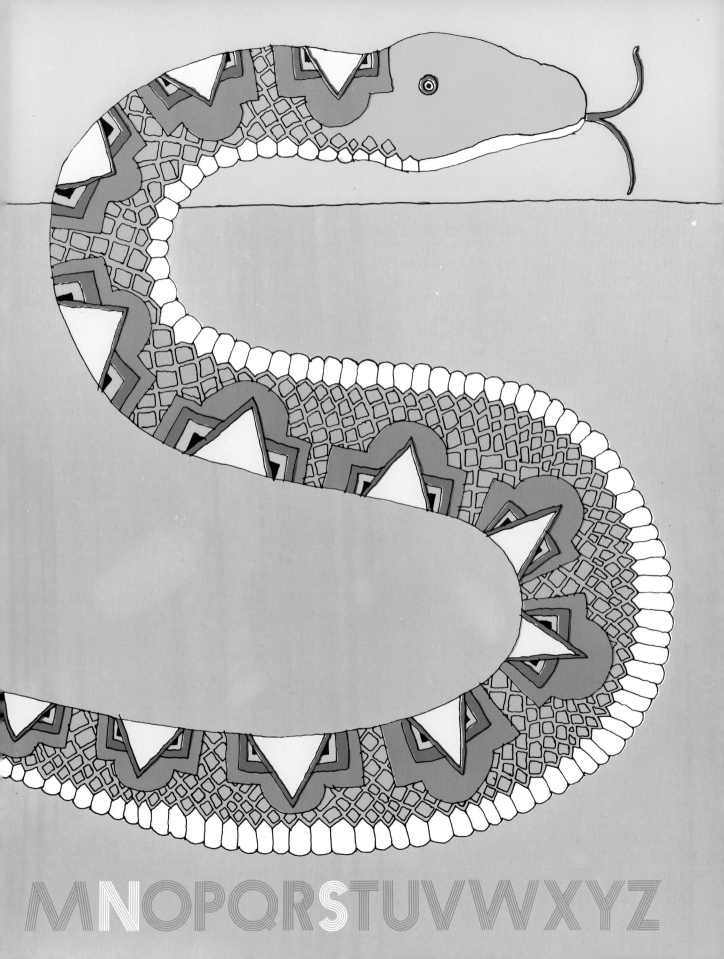

MNOPQRSTUVWXYZ

ABCDEFGHIJKLMNOPQRSTUVWXYZ

U

ABCDEFGHIJKLMN

OPQRSTUVWXYZ

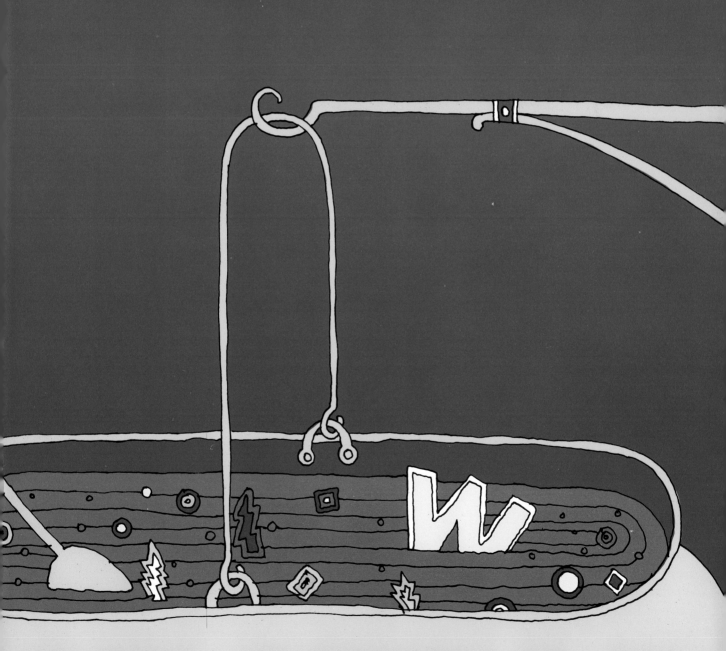

ABCDEFGHIJKLMNOPQRSTUVWXYZ

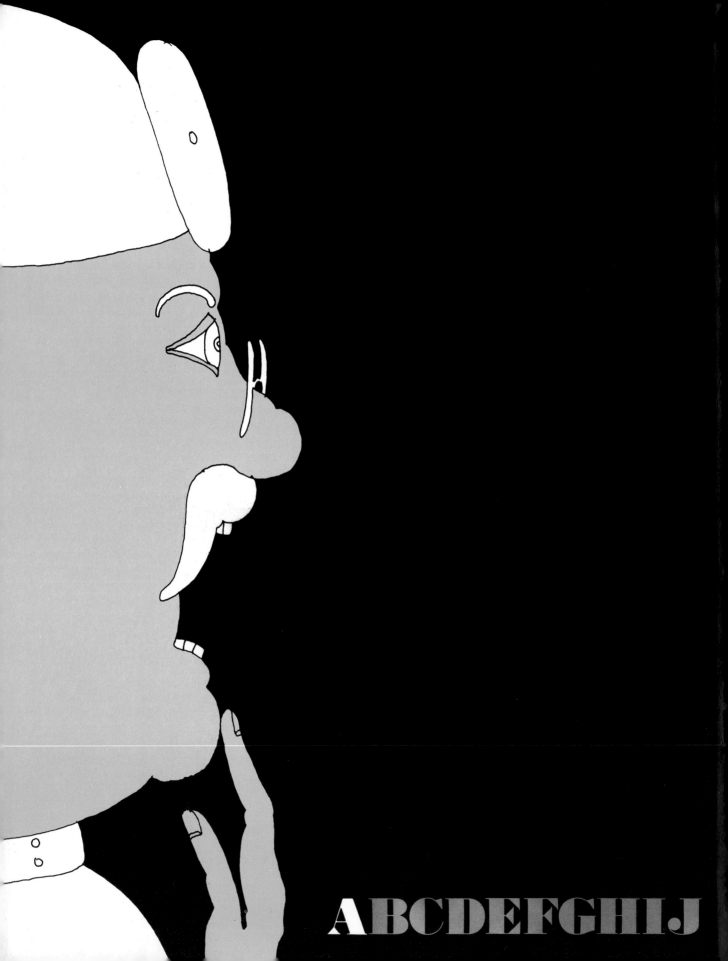

ABCDEFGHIJ

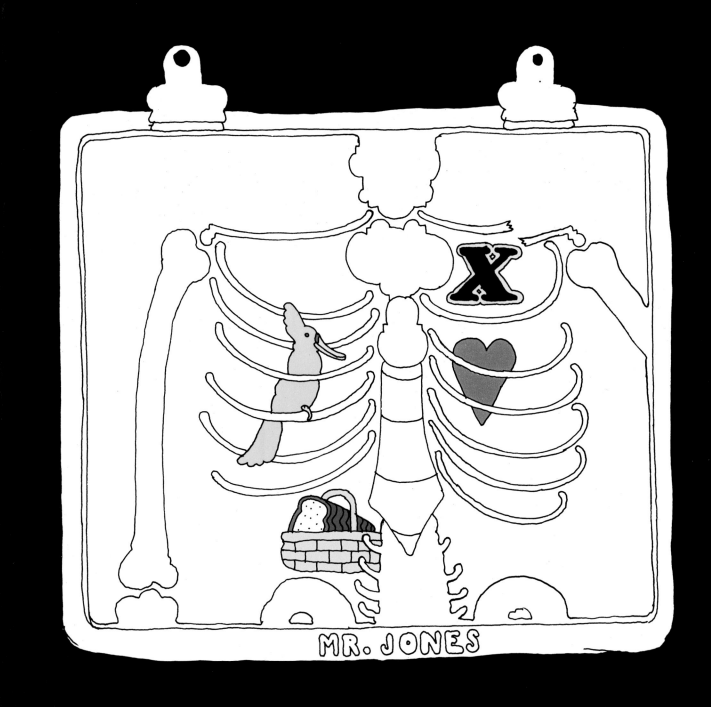

KLMNOPQRSTUVWXYZ

ABCDEFGHIJKLMNOP

QRSTUVWXYZ

ABCDEFGHIJKLMNOPQRSTUVWXYZ

If you could
not guess the words
in the alphabets
here they are.

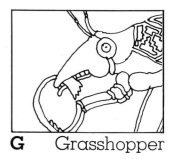

G   Grasshopper

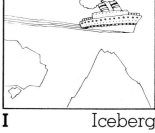

H   Hat

A   Airplane

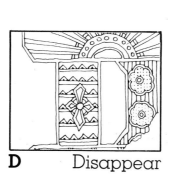

D   Disappear

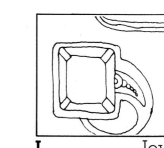

I   Iceberg

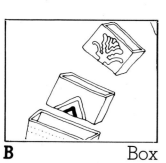

B   Box

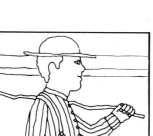

E   Evening

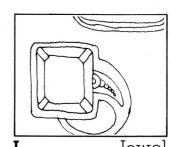

J   Jewel

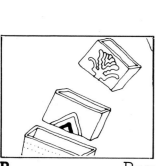

C   Cat

F   Fish

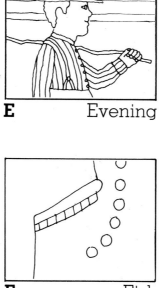

K   Knight

 **L** Lion

 **Q** Queen

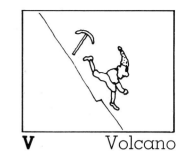 **V** Volcano

 **M** Mermaid

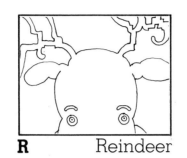 **R** Reindeer

 **W** Witch

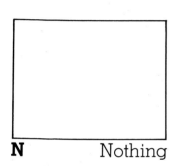 **N** Nothing

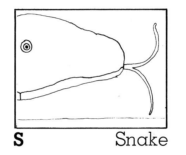 **S** Snake

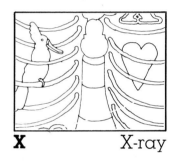 **X** X-ray

 **O** Owl

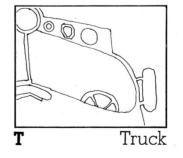 **T** Truck

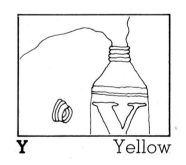 **Y** Yellow

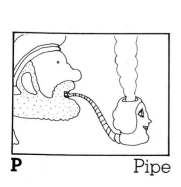 **P** Pipe

 **U** Up

 **Z** Zoo

ABCDEFGHIJKLM

ABCDEFGHIJKLM

ABCDEFGHIJKLM

ABCDEFGHIJKLM

ABCDEFGHIJKLM

ABCDEFGHIJKLM

ABCDEFGHIJKLM

ABCDEFGHIJKLM

ABCDEFGHIJKLM

ABCDEFGHIJKLM